ANIMAL SCRAMBLE

A TEMPLAR BOOK

First published in the UK in 2020 by Templar Books,
an imprint of Bonnier Books UK,
The Plaza, 535 King's Road, London, SW10 0SZ
www.templarco.co.uk
www.bonnierbooks.co.uk

1 3 5 7 9 10 8 6 4 2

ISBN 978-1-78741-491-4

This book was typeset in Chelsea Market Pro
The illustrations were created with colour pencil

Edited by Ruth Symons
Designed by Marty Cleary and Olivia Cook
Production by Emma Kidd

Printed in China

ANIMAL SCRAMBLE

Lucy Volpin

templar
books

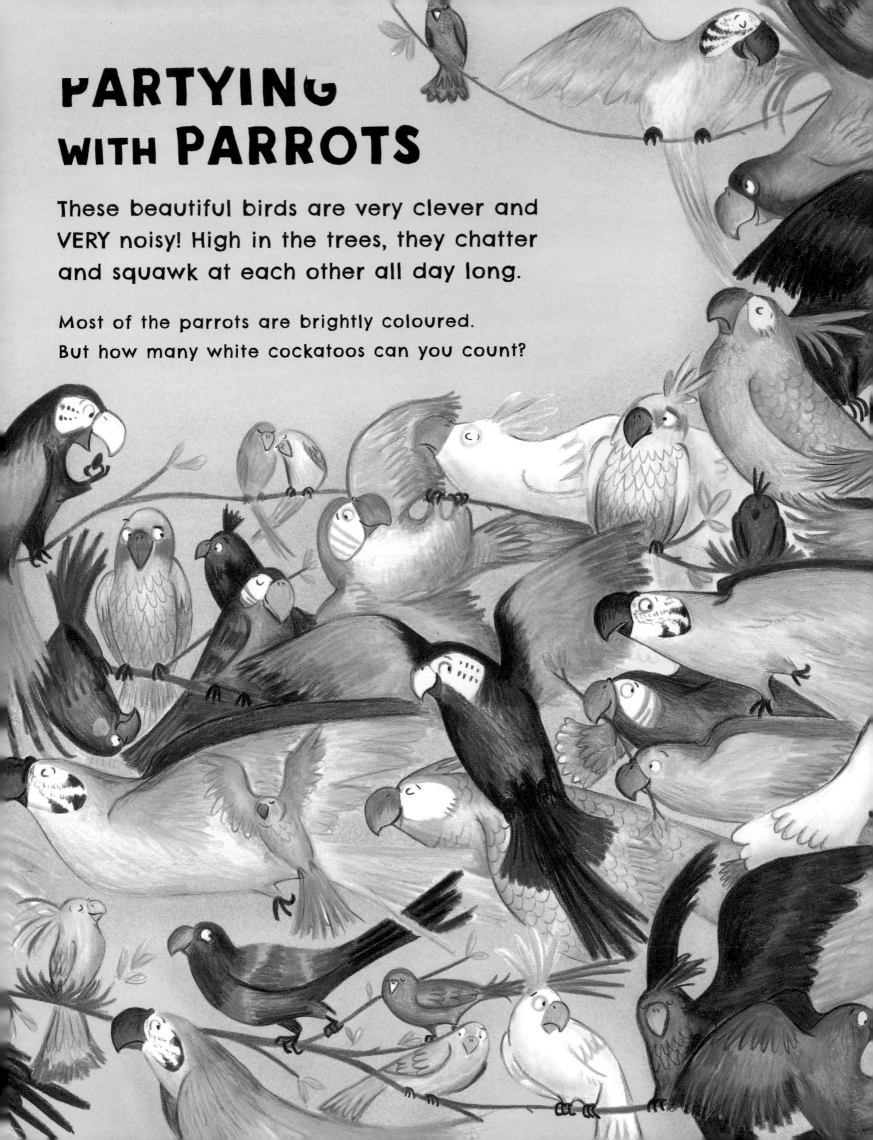

PARTYING WITH PARROTS

These beautiful birds are very clever and VERY noisy! High in the trees, they chatter and squawk at each other all day long.

Most of the parrots are brightly coloured. But how many white cockatoos can you count?

A few parrots have made nests. Where are they?

Can you see two parrots who won't share?

What colour parrot would you want to be?

FLAPPING WITH FLAMINGOS

Flamingos wade through the water looking for their favourite food — tasty shrimp. In fact, that's what makes them so perfectly pink!

Who do you think looks palest? They need to eat more shrimp!

Which flamingo is flying the wrong way?

Who looks like they need more balancing practice?

Oh dear. Which two flamingos are in a bit of a twist?

CAMPING WITH CAMELS

Camels can go for many weeks without water. Their fatty humps are like a packed lunch to keep them going – handy on long desert treks!

Some camels have one hump and others have two, but how many camels are there altogether?

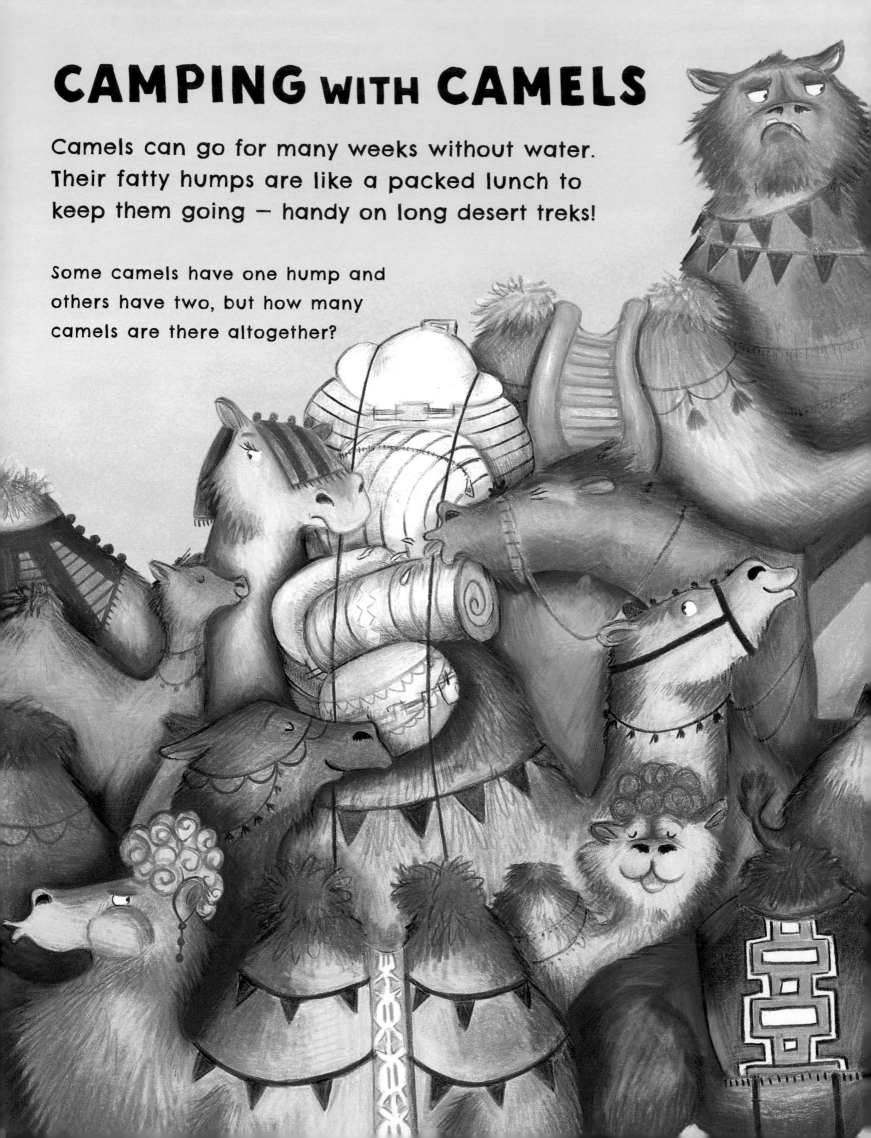

Whose outfit do you like best?

Camels like to spit – yuck! Who needs to mind their manners?

How many camels can you see with curly hair?

ZIPPING WITH ZEBRAS

Down at the watering hole, zebras stick together. Their stripes confuse predators trying to sneak up on them, and also help them to hide in the long grass.

Zebra stripes run up and down. Can you see one zebra with stripes that go from side to side instead?

Who is enjoying a grassy snack?

Who do you think has the goofiest smile?

How many zebras can you count?

FLIPPING WITH FROGS

Frogs live in damp, shady places, from tropical jungles to garden ponds. With their long, springy legs, they can jump huge distances!

Frogs use their super-sticky tongues to catch flies. How many frogs have their tongues out?

Which frog has the biggest smile?

Tree frogs have orange hands
and feet. Can you find one here?

Who has found their frog prince?

WALLOWING WITH WALRUSES

Walruses use their bristly whiskers to search for food on the ocean floor. They have two long, white tusks for fighting and digging.

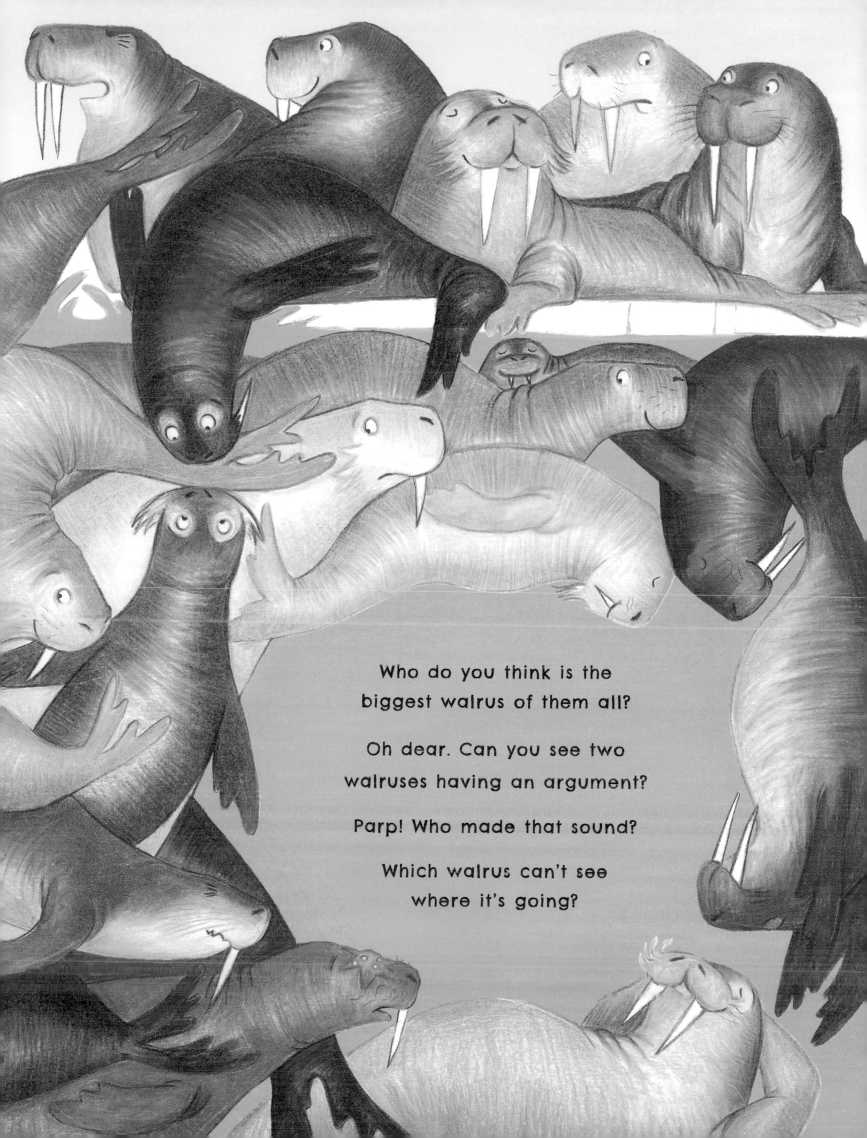

Who do you think is the
biggest walrus of them all?

Oh dear. Can you see two
walruses having an argument?

Parp! Who made that sound?

Which walrus can't see
where it's going?

ACROBATICS WITH APES

Apes like nothing more than a big family party. They play together, groom each other, share food and cuddle up for a snooze at the end of the day!

These chimpanzees, gorillas and orangutans have some amazing hairstyles. But who doesn't look too pleased with theirs?

Can you spot five different types
of fruit hidden in the scene?

How many cute babies can you count?

If you could choose, which hairstyle
would you like?

BUILDING WITH BEETLES

Scurrying among the leaves are beetles little and large — some are as big as your hand! Even the tiniest among them are incredibly strong.

How many pairs of matching beetles can you find?

Not all beetles can fly but most do.
Can you see any with their wings out?

Beetles have so many beautiful colours.
Which one is your favourite?

Where is the biggest beetle?

PLAYING WITH PENGUINS

Layers of fluffy feathers help keep penguins dry and cosy. In winter, they all huddle together to keep each other warm! Brrr...

Watch out! Which penguin is about to get hit by a snowball?

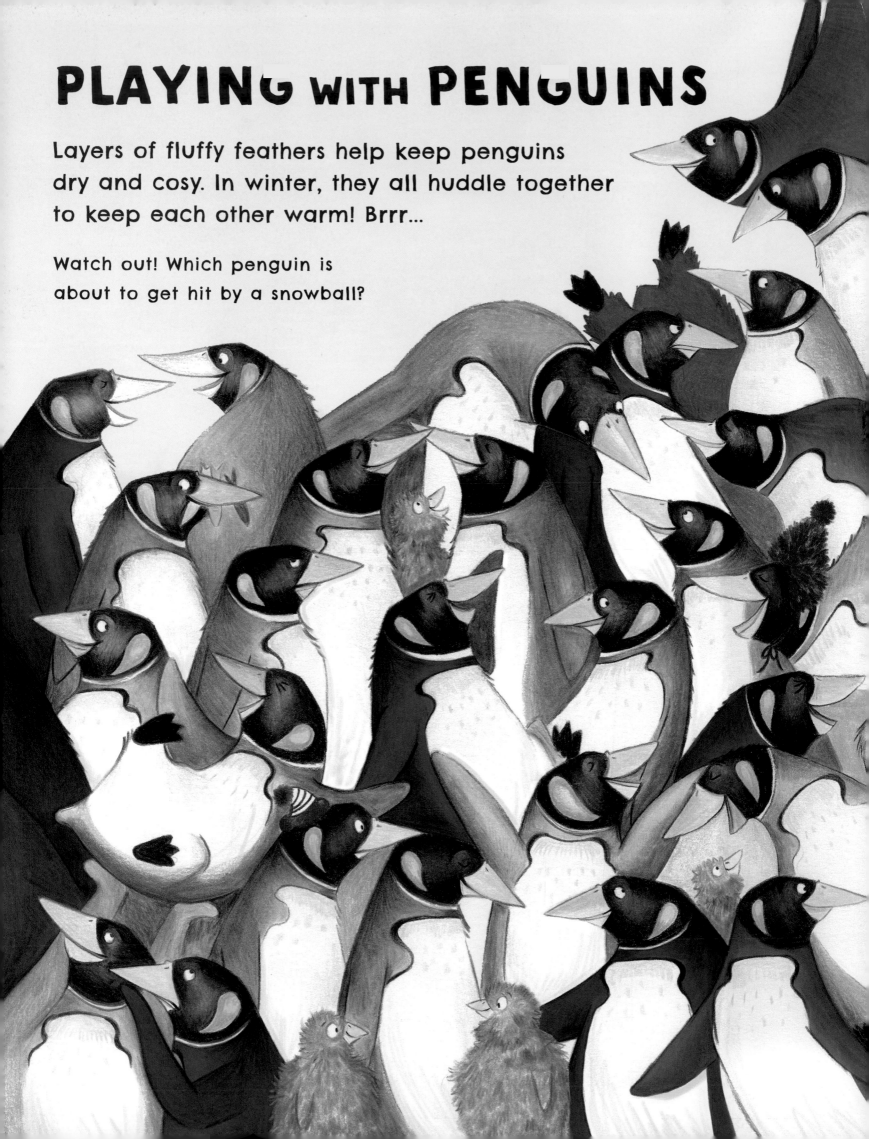

How many fluffy chicks can you spot?

Which penguin do you think looks cosiest?

Who has just made a new friend?

BOUNCING WITH BIG CATS

With their sharp claws and teeth, these big cats are some of the best hunters on the planet. When they roar, everybody runs away.

Cheetahs are the fastest animals in the world. Can you see one going for a run?

Who do you think is roaring and who is only yawning?

Male lions have big shaggy manes.
How many can you count in this scene?

Are there more stripy cats or spotty cats?

FROLICKING WITH FISH

Lots of colourful fish live on the coral reef, where the water is nice and warm. They swim in groups called schools.

Clownfish like to keep together, but can you spot one that's lost?

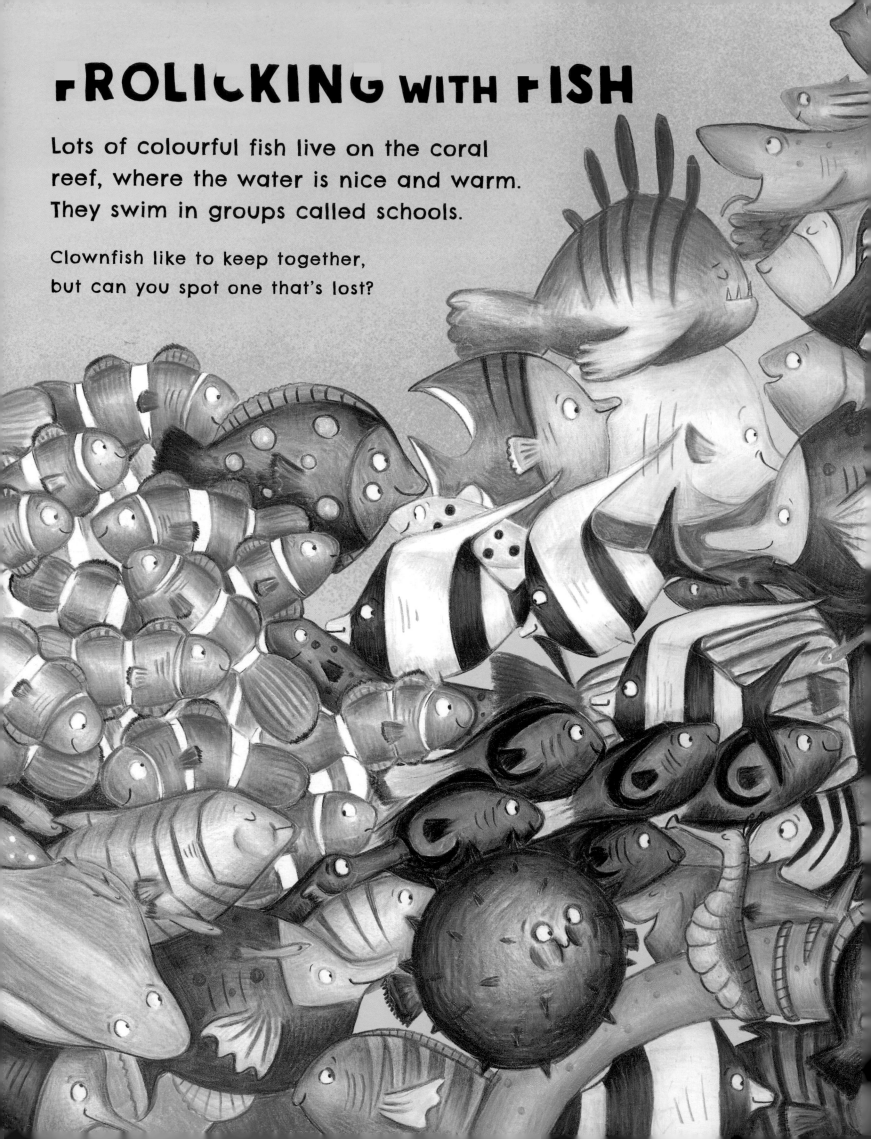

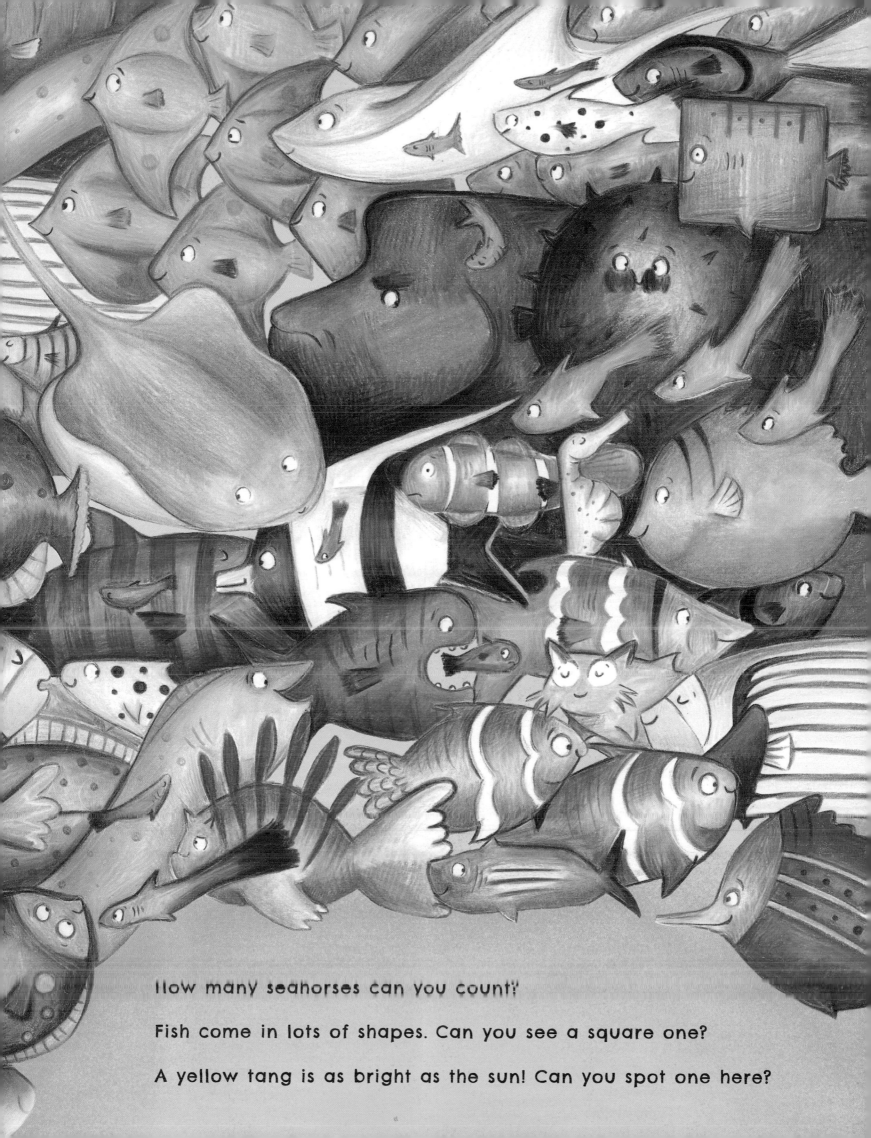

How many seahorses can you count?

Fish come in lots of shapes. Can you see a square one?

A yellow tang is as bright as the sun! Can you spot one here?

WANDERING WITH WOLVES

Wolves live in big family groups called packs.
To talk to each other or warn away strangers,
they let out a long, loud HOOOOWL!

Everyone's making a lot of noise.
Which wolf wishes it was quieter?

Which two wolves are
playing a game of tug-of-war?

Who do you think is leader of the pack?

How many fluffy tails can you count?

SWIMMING
WITH SHARKS

Sharks come in all shapes and sizes, from toothy great whites to tiny dogfish. However big or small, they have LOTS of razor-sharp teeth!

Who just finished a fish supper?
Hint: they need to brush their teeth!

Can you find five sharks in diving goggles?

How many hammerhead sharks can you see?

Which creature has hitched a ride on one of the sharks?

SLITHERING WITH SNAKES

Stripy, spotty or diamond-patterned, snakes have bold markings and bright colours to warn that they are dangerous.

Rattlesnakes love to shake their tails. How many shaking tails are there?

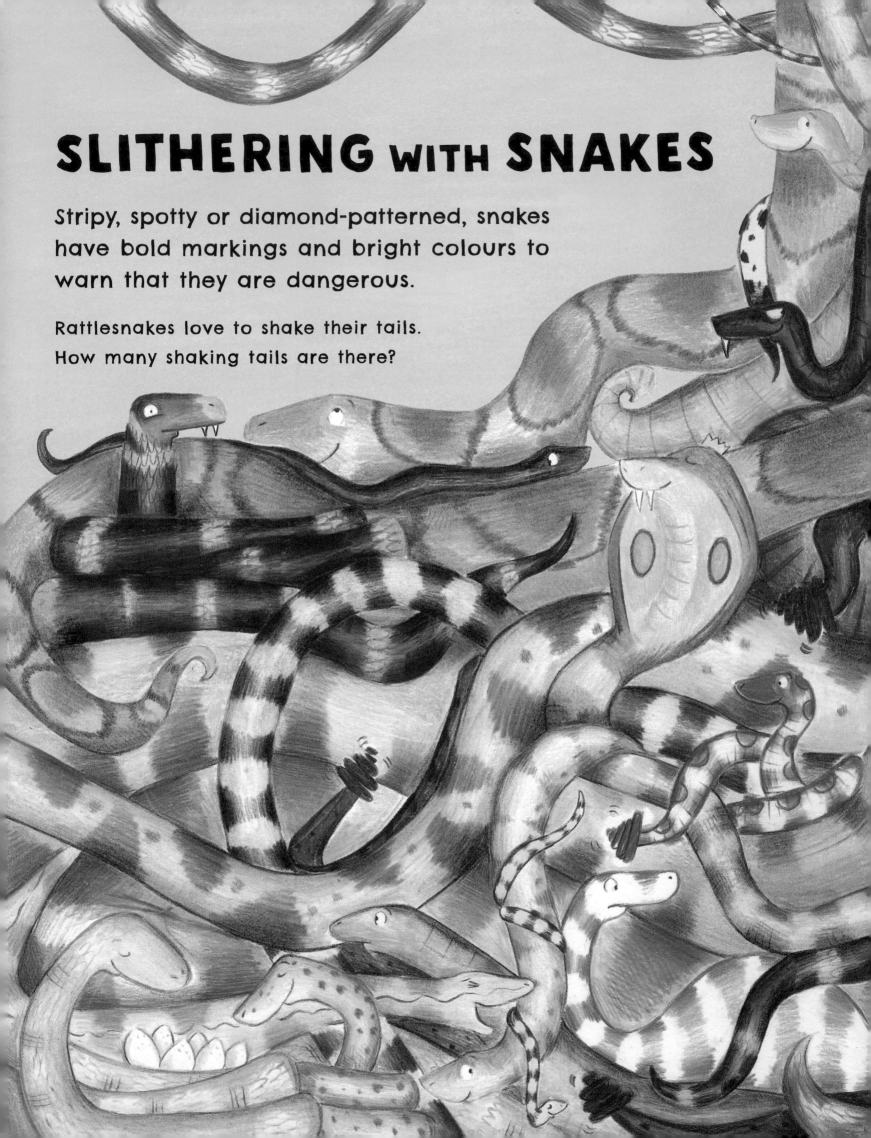

What a tummy! Who has had a BIG lunch?

Which snake do you think looks scariest?

Can you spot the king cobra?
Look for his crown!

NOW IT'S UP TO YOU!

Would you prefer fur, feathers or scales?

Out of the sky, the ground and the sea,
where would you prefer to be?

If you were an animal would you whinny
like a zebra or roar like a lion?

Do you have a favourite animal from this book?
Which animal is it and why?

Some of these animals have very funny faces.
Can you pull a face to look like them?